Everybody's Special

Written & Illustrated by
Tamara Rattigan

First Published in Great Britain 2015
by Burst Universe, England.

Copyright © 2015 Tamara Rattigan

A CIP catalogue record for this book is available
from the British Library

ISBN 978-0-9933661-0-9

1 3 5 9 10 8 6 4 3 2

Printed in China

Some of us have blue eyes

Others have
brown and green

Mummy says that my eyes are the loveliest she's seen!

Some of us have blonde hair

Others brown or red

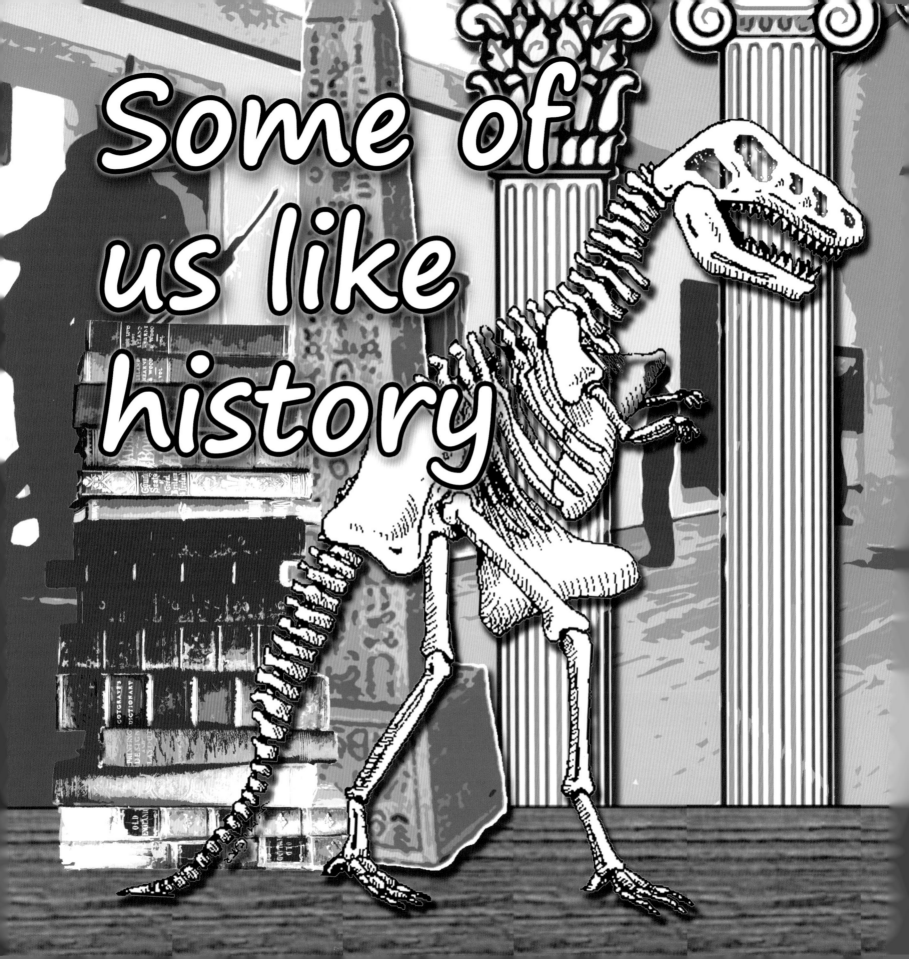

And some of us like art

Some of us have long, long long legs which make us very Tall

Some of us have little legs that make us short and **small**

Some of us have lots of teeth. My baby sister has just *two!*

My friend she wears a brace on hers to make them straight and new

to help us
see much better

Some of us have dark skin

whilst others like to run

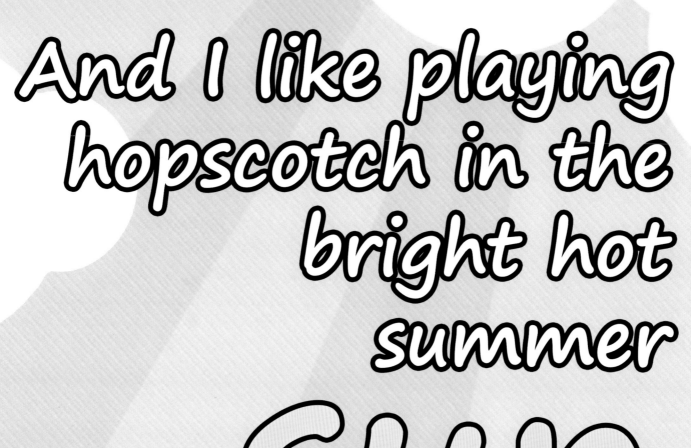

And I like playing hopscotch in the bright hot summer **SUN**

In the way we look and the things we do

Because each of these
unique features

For three very special little people
Kiah, Poppy & Otis
x